W.T. GRAHAM
21st September 1996

NEWPORT
TRANSPORTER BRIDGE

A Guide to its History, Construction and Operation

Falcon D Hildred

Newport
COUNTY BOROUGH

BWRDEISTREF SIROL
Casnewydd

A Newport Museum & Art Gallery Book

First published in Great Britain in 1996 by
Newport County Borough Council

Editor
Roger Cucksey
Newport Museum & Art Gallery

Design
Falcon D Hildred

Production
John Hilton
Graphic Design Unit

Photography
Rex Moreton

ISBN 0 9519136 4 6

Introduction

From earliest times until the great transport improvements of the 19th Century, rivers were a vital part of the transport network. They were also often serious obstacles to those whose paths crossed them. It is very easy nowadays to take bridges for granted, but in the days before highway and river authorities with power and money to build and maintain bridges, the only means of crossing was often by ford or ferry. As these generally suffered from neglect and conflicting private interests, they were frequent causes of delay, discomfort and even danger. Nevertheless, the importance placed on keeping open these lines of communication can be seen today in two quite different structures along the River Usk at Newport, both within two miles (3·2 km) of each other yet separated by seven centuries. One, a typically solid example of 12th Century military engineering - the Castle; the other, a typically inventive example of 19th Century civil engineering - the Transporter Bridge. The castle gave Newport its name, and the bridge became the symbol identified with that name.

This guide explains why such an unusual bridge was built, and then takes the reader on a tour of the structure, explaining its construction and workings with the aid of a sequence of drawings. These drawings also record the bridge as it was in 1988, prior to the modifications which were carried out as part of the refurbishment of 1992/95.

Above: The Transporter Bridge
Above right: Newport Castle and Town Bridge

Newport's Origins

Newport, South Wales, is situated on the River Usk about four miles (6·4 km) from where it joins the Bristol Channel. Contrary to what one may expect, the town does not get its name from the flourishing seaport which sprang up in the 19th Century, but from the New Fort or castle, built to defend both the entrance to the river, and the ford which carried through it the road between England and South Wales. There had been a fort here from pre-Roman times. The first bridge on the site - a wooden one - was built in the 12th Century by the Normans, and it was around this and the castle walls that in time a small town with riverside quays gathered. In 1800, Newport - or to give it its proper Welsh name Casnewydd (Newcastle) - had changed very little from a medieval town, comprising still of around only 120 houses and a population of just over 1,000.

Below: High Street, Newport, about 1900

By 1900 however, the population had increased to over 67,000. The event that sparked off this explosion was the Industrial Revolution. Beneath the hills and valleys just to the north, lay a vast wealth of coal and iron-ore, and Newport, along with other South Wales ports, was ideally placed to ship these much valued commodities around the coast to other parts of Britain, and, of course, abroad. The vital artery which brought down this wealth and thereby laid the foundation of the town as a major seaport, was the Monmouthshire Canal opened in 1796. All manner of improvements for the speedy and efficient handling of goods then followed. In 1850 the South Wales Railway opened, its bridge over the Usk skimming past the ramparts of the castle, which by now was a picturesque ruin partly used as a brewery. Then between 1842 and 1875, two deep-water docks enclosed by lock gates were dug out and soon enlarged on land beside the river. Known at first as 'wet' or 'floating' docks to distinguish them from open harbours which ran dry at low tide, these provided safe deep water on which vessels could be moved and handled day and night regardless of tide and weather.

A Monmouthshire Canal
B Castle and Town Bridge
C Town Dock
D Transporter Bridge
E Orb Ironworks
F Alexandra Docks
G South Lock
H George Street Bridge (1964)

Bristol Channel

Detail from a map of 1901 showing some of the riverside wharves which extended from the Town Bridge for two miles (3·2 km) down stream along the west bank. Brithdir Wharf, which is just visible at the bottom, was to become the site of the western tower of the Transporter Bridge.

Need for a Second Crossing

By 1880 the town had extended across to the east bank, and it was realised that a second crossing would soon be needed. This was in order to ease congestion on the Town Bridge, and to open up the industrial potential of the east bank, by providing a more direct link further downstream with the docks and southern end of town on the west side. These matters were spurred on in 1896 by competition with nearby Barry Docks, to provide a site for the Orb Iron Works (at that time John Lysaghts Ltd), which for many years was the most important manufacturer in Newport. By this time the Usk was busier than at any time in history, being used not only by steamers that were getting progressively larger, but also still, by tall-masted sailing ships, all needing every bit of available room - and wind- to pass and turn, and to negotiate the four miles (6·4 km) of tight bends. Added to this was the river's unusually high tides - frequently around 47 ft (14·3 m) - resulting in a swift current which ebbed and flowed four times daily, and left a narrow channel between extensive mud banks at low water. All this prompted much debate as to what form this second crossing should take, but it was clear from the start that nothing should be considered which would limit headroom or hinder navigation in any way.

The Options

A small privately owned rowing-boat ferry already operated at a convenient point about two miles (3·2 km) downstream. However, because of the nature of the river, this had proved inconvenient. Also an accident involving loss of life had occurred. A ferry would in any case have needed piers extending out to the low-water channel. Development of this facility was therefore ruled out, as was also a conventional bridge. Bridges of lift or swing design were unsuitable, because the width of the river was beyond what could be spanned without the use of fixed sections which would have encroached on the shipping lanes. Schemes for a tunnel were prepared including one for pedestrians only. Although Parliamentary Consent for such a tunnel was obtained in 1889, this option was shelved as the cost was considered far too high when balanced against the benefits foreseeable at that time. The crossing, after all, was not part of the national transport network. It was only needed to improve local communications. Cost also ruled out a high-level road bridge as this would have been a massive structure requiring long approach viaducts at a gradient of 1 in 20, in order to gain mast clearance from the low-lying land.

A New Type of Design Chosen

Hemmed in by these difficulties, the matter remained unresolved until the Borough engineer, Robert Haynes, heard of an entirely new method of crossing which had been developed and successfully put to use on the Continent. Evidently other ports were experiencing similar problems. This new concept, known as a Transporter Bridge, was a combination of bridge and ferry. It was designed by the French engineer, Ferdinand Arnodin. Judged from today's perspective we may question the sense of so much iron and steel to carry so small a vessel, but in the context of things at that time, it met all the requirements. People in those days were used to ferries and the problems and limitations inherent in their operation. What Arnodin did was literally lift his ferry above those problems, so that it could glide smoothly from shore to shore in a direct and level line, regardless of tide or mud, and without having to turn and tie up. Thus, what had hitherto often been an inconvenient part of the journey, was now for many made into a pleasant interlude. It provided a reliable and, for its day, rapid crossing; its carrying capacity matched estimated needs; it presented no hazard to shipping; and because of the relative lightness of the whole structure, its cost was well within the Borough's resources. It was the only proposal which provided what was needed within all the constraints. Nevertheless, it took all Haynes' efforts and a visit to Rouen by a strong delegation of Council officials to inspect the bridge there, to get the scheme accepted. The site chosen for the bridge was the same as that used by the ferry and selected for the proposed tunnel. Parliamentary Consent was obtained in 1900. Haynes and Arnodin were joint engineers, and construction was carried out by Alfred Thorne of Westminster at a cost of £98,000. Work began in 1902, and the bridge was opened with due ceremony on 12 September 1906 by Viscount Tredegar.

Left: The Ferry in 1902

General View

A transporter bridge is a structure which carries a suspended or aerial ferry. This ferry is held above the water, at road level, from a high-level beam set clear of the tallest ships. In Newport the ferry is known as the Gondola; the moving carriage from which it is suspended is called the Traveller; and the beam along which this runs, is the Boom. The Traveller is pulled to and fro by cable from the Motor-house built over the eastern approach road. The key plan on page 23 shows the general layout of the bridge as a whole, and names its principal parts.

The two views to the right here are from the east bank looking across to the town. The original Town Dock and riverside quays were upstream to the right. The timber remains of some of these quays may still be seen in places. The building with the red tower is the Waterloo public house.

The building above the road is the motor house. The stairway up the right leg of the tower leads to the public walkways along the boom. There are 277 steps. The corresponding stair from the opposite bank is on the left, thereby encouraging a one-way flow in each direction, and so reducing the need to pass on the rather narrow walkways.

Designed by F Arnodin of France. Opened 1906.
Span 645 ft (196m). Headroom 177 ft (54m).
Capacity 6 cars + 120 people each 7½ minutes.

Newport Transporter Bridge.

5

Anchorages and Workshop

The main cables are fixed in massive Anchorages, each formed of 2,200 tons (2,235·2 tonnes) of masonry built above ground on a concrete raft with timber piles set about 8° off vertical to resist slip. Lean-to sheds attached to these serve as stores. They contained the usual mixture of spares, junk, and such redundant items as one of the original navigation lights, old bellows for the workshop forge, and a basket used for raising men and tools during construction (shown on page 13). The modern equivalent of this basket is shown suspended from the far anchorage cable. In the distance, extra high pylons lift electricity power lines clear of shipping. All the navigation lights are now electric, both mains and battery powered.

Beside the eastern anchorage is the timber-framed, corrugated-iron and brick Workshop which provides a base for the maintenance crew: John McDermott, Bill Collier and others. At the far end, old chairs and bits of car and caravan upholstery have been utilised to form a snug corner by a rusting coke stove. Just visible in the gloom and clutter to the left, are the graceful curves of 'The Denbigh' drilling machine. On the bench by the window among tools, teacups and The Daily Mirror, a pair of field glasses enables distant parts of the bridge to be brought into closer view.

Top : Driving timber piles for anchorage
Above: Anchorage nearing completion
Left: John McDermott (left) and Bill Collier Photo F D Hildred

Anchorage/Store & Workshop

Drill

Old Navigation lamp, Electrical Locker & Bellows

The Motor-house

This contains the haulage machinery for pulling the traveller to and fro. Power is provided by two 35 horse-power electric motors, manufactured by The Lancashire Dynamo & Motor Co Ltd, which incorporate an automatic braking system. Bearings are automatically lubricated by oil-bottles which not only removes the need to keep going round with an oil can, but also shows clearly when topping up is needed. Normally, the machinery is controlled from the gondola, but this facility is duplicated in the motor house for maintenance purposes and in case of emergency. Also, if the need arose, the bridge could still operate on just one motor. The main electrical supply comes from the west bank by cable over the bridge, and there is also a back-up supply from the east bank in case of breakdown. Hatches are provided in the floor for the replacement of machinery.

The haulage cables pass from the drum through slots in the roof. Slots are necessary as the cables move sideways as they wind and unwind. To guide them through these slots, is a cable carriage running on tracks in the roof. Attached to this on the outside are two broad strips of metal called wings. These cover the slots and so prevent rain getting in. The cables pass through small holes in these wings. This carriage must have looked a curious contraption when it was taking shape on the workbench, and when compared to the kind of aircraft that were flying round at that time, it is easy to see why it came to be known as 'The Aeroplane'.

The motor house is a good place from which to examine the designs of three types of balustrade used in the bridge. The strongest of these is the riveted lattice girder of the roadway below, which is both guardrail and part of the supporting structure for this short bridged section. Cheapest, was the expanded mesh* of the tower stairways, made by cutting slits into sheet metal, then stretching the sheet so that the slits open into diamond-shaped holes. Most pleasing though, is the balustrade of the motor-house itself, ingeniously formed by simply putting a kink in thin metal strip, then forming it into a weave.

* replaced in the 1994 refurbishment

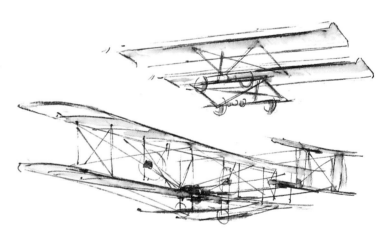

Top right: Nameplate on the haulage motors Photo F D Hildred
Bottom right: The cable carriage and a typical aeroplane of around 1905

Motor House

Cable Carriage or 'Aeroplane'

Oil Bottle

Balustrades

Electric Haulage Motor

Barriers and Buffer

All the ironwork of the barriers is of standard components throughout. The turnstile is controlled by a foot-operated lever which engages in slots cut into the base of the spindle at each quarter turn. When the lever is released, a spherical weight causes it to drop into the next slot, thus locking the turnstile. A rectangular hole in the top of the turnstile originally housed a counting mechanism.

Once through the barrier, one passes over a shallow ramp of planks bound with metal. This is a sliding Buffer which absorbs any impact from the gondola that may occur whilst it is docking. The leading end projects beyond the jetty, and is supported by rollers running on short lengths of girder. The rear end rests on steel slides. A 2-ton weight suspended from the projecting edge returns the buffer to its extended position after use. The whole is held in position by its own weight.

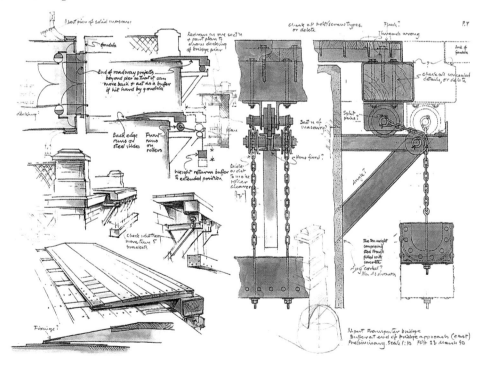

The Gondola

Almost everything about the bridge is uncompromisingly functional. Only those parts which passengers come into close contact with have any form of embellishment: the gates, parts of the motor house, and of course, the gondola which, with its red and white lifebelts and kingfisher blue paintwork, has all the gaiety of a seaside pavilion. It measures 33 ft long by 40 ft wide (10m x 12·2m). Suspension cables, raked as on a ship to brace the gondola against being swung about by the wind, add to the nautical feel. A weather vane helps the driver to take account of the force and direction of any wind, as this can have a marked affect on the gondola's movements. And finally, dagger-boards form a decorative fringe to the roofs of open-sided passenger areas fitted with slatted iron seats. Cold comfort by today's standards, but people were used to it then, and most passengers would have been workmen anyway. Chains originally closed off the ends of the gondola whilst it was in motion, but an ungainly pair of modern gates does this now. The cables which carry the gondola, although maybe appearing slender, provide the same generous margin of safety as all the other cablework on the bridge, which in principle is calculated to have a breaking strain of up to five times its working load. To ensure that each cable is taking its correct weight, they are all fixed by means of U-bolts which allow for adjusting the tension. They also allow for complete replacement of individual cables without having to close the bridge. The extent to which Arnodin believed in such ease of replacement, is shown in his transporter bridge for Bizerta in Tunisia, which was entirely dismantled and rebuilt at Brest.

Left: Preliminary study of buffer

10

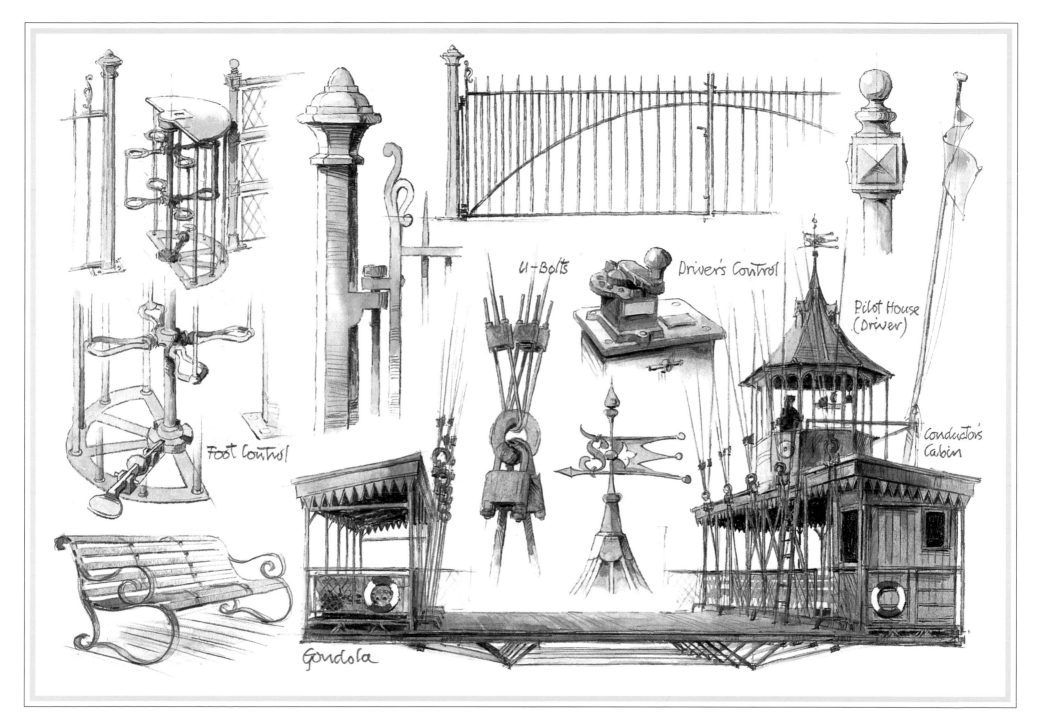

Foot Control

U-Bolts

Driver's Control

Pilot House
(Driver)

Conductor's
Cabin

Gondola

The Towers and Boom

The base of the tower shows how all the weight of the bridge has been gathered together so as to bear down on the centre core of the foundation piers where they are strongest. All the rivets would have been applied red-hot by men working in pairs, one man holding the rivet in position while the other closed it with a hammer and a shaping tool known as a snap. A third person, usually a boy, had the job of heating the rivets in a portable brazier and supplying them to the teams in his vicinity.

For the convenience of maintenance men working on the remote upper levels of the bridge, a toilet and a toolshed were provided. The toilet, located centrally on the boom above mid-stream, was a tiny and very basic structure of timber and corrugated-iron, fitted with a plank seat with space behind, and a sliding door. The toolshed, also of corrugated-iron, was on the steel deck of the east tower. Both were removed in the refurbishment. The two sheds together, were referred to by some of the men as 'The Pent-house Suite'.

Prior to the refurbishment, a hand-operated winch stood on the platform of the west tower. It is not likely to have served much purpose, however, as electrical winches and cranes were used throughout construction.

It will be noticed from the view of the cable saddles at the tops of the towers, that to prevent wear and facilitate individual replacement, the main suspension and anchor cables are not continuous, but join at this point. The lighter raking cables are, however, continuous. The access platforms round the saddles were added in 1994.

Above right: The eastern tower as it was in 1988 Photo F D Hildred
Below right: View from deck of traveller Photo F D Hildred

12

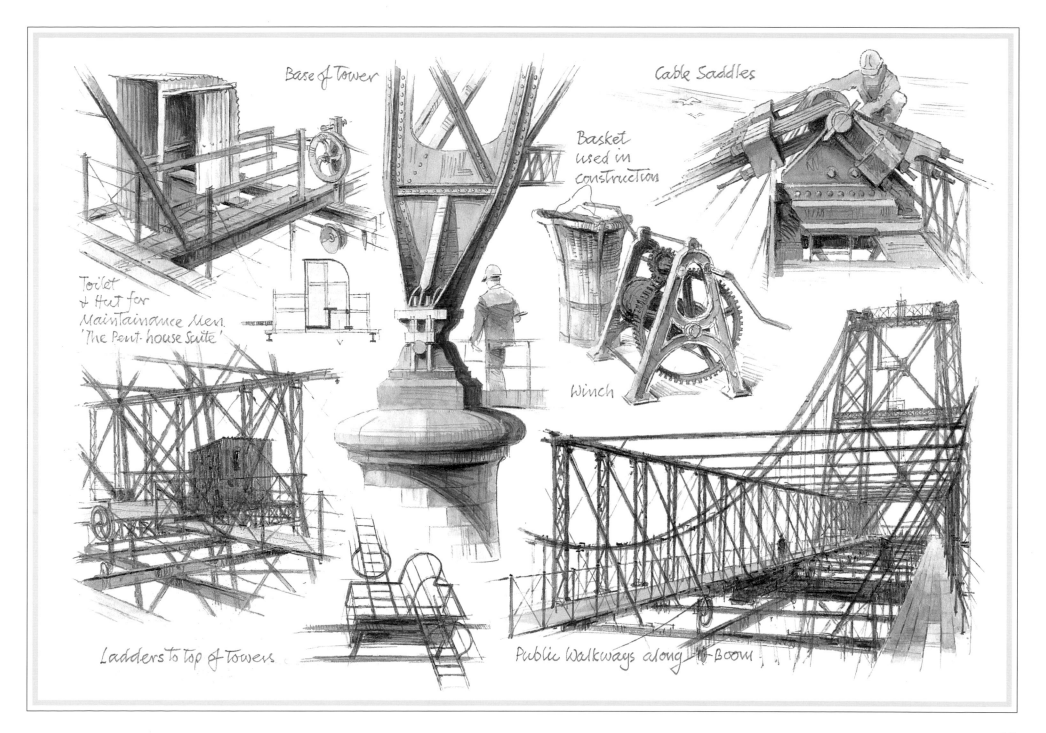

Base of Tower

Cable Saddles

Basket used in construction

Toilet & Hut for Maintainance Men. 'The Pent-house Suite'

Winch

Ladders to top of Towers

Public Walkways along Boom

Details

Whereas the towers are rigid structures, built up of standard steel sections riveted together, the boom is designed to adjust to climatic change and the weight of the traveller as it moves to and fro. It is therefore not fixed to the towers, but suspended from them, and where it passes through them, is held at the sides by greased rubbing strips which allow it to move lengthwise. As will be seen more clearly in the drawing on page 23, two suspension systems are used. The portions near the towers, are supported by raking cables which fan out from the tower tops. The central portion hangs from the main catenary cables on suspension rods which, being of wrought-iron, used the traditional blacksmith's skill of heat-welding. As the traveller moves along the bridge, its weight causes the boom to dip slightly. In order to allow for this movement, the top girder is fitted at three points along its length with sprung expansion joints.

Arnodin took full advantage of the tensile strength of cable to give the boom its required stiffness. Its sides are braced almost along their entire length by diagonals pulling against vertical stanchions which, interestingly, are not fixed top and bottom, but simply located on lengths of rod. Where cables cross each other, they are protected from chafing by replaceable wear plates held on by wire binding. Such extensive use of cable, even to the guardrails of the walkways all resulted in a considerable saving in weight, but it offered no comfort to anyone nervous of heights! The drawing on the opposite page shows the method used throughout the bridge, for ensuring a perfectly safe fixing of the cables into the blocks, by simply doubling over their ends and setting them in lead.

As the boom carries what is in effect an electrically-powered cable-hauled railway, there are a considerable number of components and moving parts which need to be checked regularly. Maintenance platforms have therefore been provided wherever necessary, and it is principally for this purpose that the walkways along the entire length of the boom and across the ends were provided. These walkways were supported alternately on the cross girders of the main underframe, and on cantilevered brackets. The latter were made from lengths of T-bar fixed at one end to the main side girder, and braced up at the projecting end by the diagonal cables of the walkway guardrails. Fixing of the 3" (75mm) thick walkway planks was by nuts and bolts with blank countersunk heads. These walkways were, however, extensively modified in the 1994 refurbishment. The traveller still retains its original timber decking.

Right: Details of boom side and original walkway

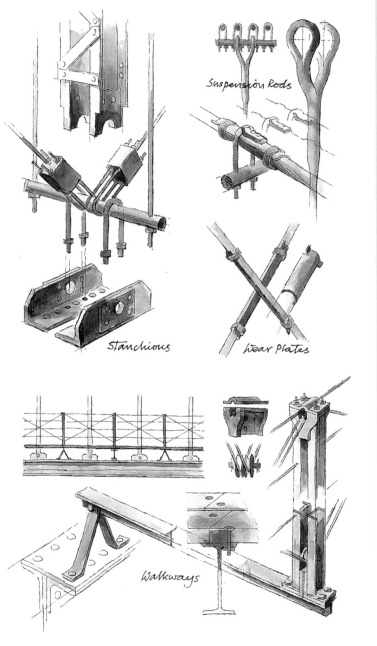

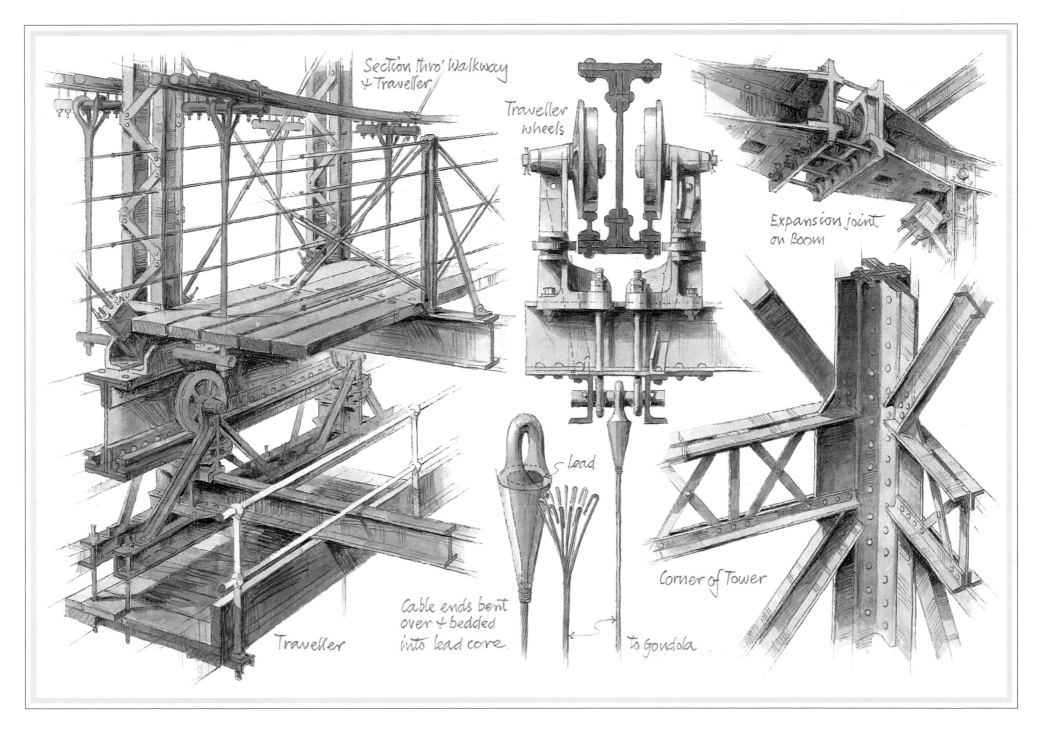

Section thro' Walkway & Traveller

Traveller wheels

Expansion joint on Boom

Traveller

Cable ends bent over & bedded into lead core.

lead

to Gondola

Corner of Tower

15

In order that the weight of the traveller is spread as much as possible on the boom, it is over three times the length of the gondola. This also provides a broad area of support from which to hang the gondola, thereby ensuring as much as possible a smooth crossing for its passengers. The traveller runs on four lengths of railway track bolted to the lower flanges of the main girder. In order to provide a level bedding for the rails, the rivets beneath are countersunk and overlaid by a packing of rubber strip. Originally, layers of hessian and lead were used. There are 60 wheels, grouped in 15 pairs on each side, with a cable to the gondola from each pair. Smaller guide wheels run along the side edges of the girder.

The haulage cables are received from the motor house and returned by large pulley-wheels at each end of the boom. The pulley at the western end was covered by a structure of wood and corrugated-iron. Along the boom, the cables are supported by sets of intermediate pulleys fixed at intervals to the spine. One of these sets is shown below, and beside the toilet illustrated on page 13. To prevent the cables being blown sideways off these pulleys the upper cable is held down by a small roller. The lower cable passes between short tails of metal, known as pendulums, which are bolted loosely to the spine. The cables are fixed to the centre of the traveller by an A-frame or tripod with a tongue of metal projecting sideways from the top. This tongue passes over the lower intermediate pulley, clearing it by about 3/4" (2 cm). As it strikes the pendulums, they swing out of the way then drop back again.

Below left: Fixing of haulage cables to traveller
Below right: Haulage pulleys at end of boom

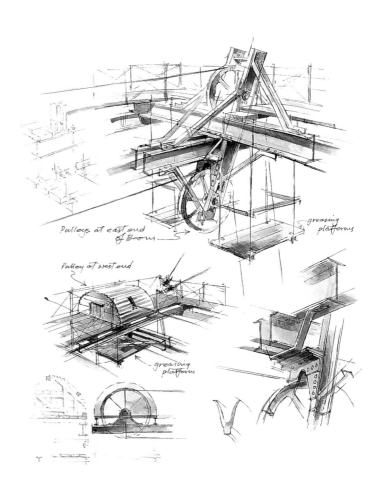

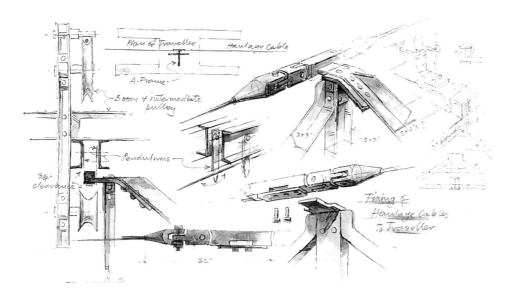

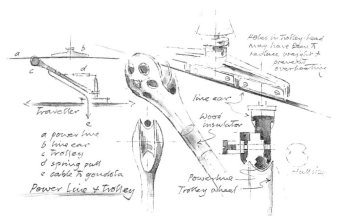

The gondola is controlled from the pilot house, using virtually the same system as a tram for picking up the overhead electrical power and regulating the speed. The driver, who is traditionally standing, increases and reduces the speed by turning the handle on one of the controllers. There are two of these, one at each end of the pilot house, so that the driver is always facing the direction of travel. From here, insulated cables run up to six trolley-wheels mounted on top of the traveller. These are made of brass and are grooved to run along exposed power lines or trolley wires of copper bar fixed just off-centre along the boom (*above*). The final link from these to the motor-house, is then made by another set of insulated cables, this time running down the eastern tower.

The power lines are fixed at intervals along the boom by line ears. These are grooved into the power lines so that they do not dislodge the trolley-wheels as they pass by. Likewise, the trolley-wheels are contained in smooth rounded trolley-heads so that if one does come off the power line, there are no sharp parts that will snag on anything or cause damage.

Above: Details of trolley head and power lines
Right: Four of the original design drawings Photo Rex Moreton

As with all things, the closer one looks at the bridge, the more one realises how much thought and effort went into its creation. Every detail from the caissons used to sink the foundations and still buried beneath them, to the delicately ornate iron ridge which finishes off the motor house roof, had to be worked out by someone. It may all look straightforward and obvious now, but there is nothing to show all the time spent in searching for these answers, comparing alternatives, and trying to anticipate all the consequences. Even the finished design drawings are no more than the tip of the iceberg. Only the countless sheets of calculations and preliminary sketches that were no doubt produced, would reveal all this effort. It will be of interest to those with experience of construction sites, to learn that the original design drawings were not on large sheets of paper, but on long strips which concertina down to A4. This would have made them much easier to refer to on a lofty and exposed location where there would usually be a strong wind blowing and at best only a plank or girder to rest on. Also the use of a French design on British soil must have added to the problems, not only because of the need to convert everything from metric to imperial, but also because of having to use British steel sections which were marginally larger and heavier than those specified. With such complex calculations necessary, one can begin to see that the dimension of 644' 10¾", given as the distance at which the towers should be set apart, was maybe not unduly finicky after all!

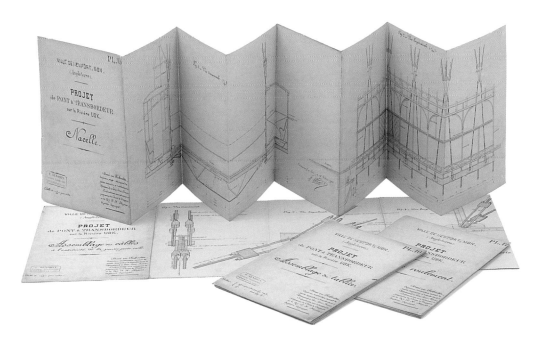

Construction

Prior to construction, and in order to obtain an accurate picture for what would be needed for the foundations, two independent site investigations were carried out and then compared for agreement. In order to reach bedrock, foundations for the towers go down in some cases as far as 86 feet (26m) - which is the equivalent of nearly halfway from road level to the underside of the boom. They were sunk by compressed air caissons. Each of these was like a huge funnel 20 feet (6m) across made of steel and concrete, and placed upside-down on the river-bed. The spout, which was about 6 feet (2m) in diameter, rose above the high water mark and provided access to the working chamber (*right*). The men inside worked under compressed air, excavating downwards in stages and removing the ground from beneath the cutting edge of the funnel or caisson. At the end of each day, the air pressure was reduced, thus allowing the caisson to sink slowly down under its own weight. A circular stone wall was then built on the top outer edge of the caisson to form a lining to the excavated shaft, and as the caisson sank, so this lining was carried down with it. The top was then progressively extended upwards to keep level with the temporary timber staging built out from the river bank. When a firm bottom had been reached, the inner access shaft was removed, and the whole space within the working chamber and masonry shaft lining was filled with concrete. It is believed this was the first time that compressed air had been used for this purpose over in Britain.

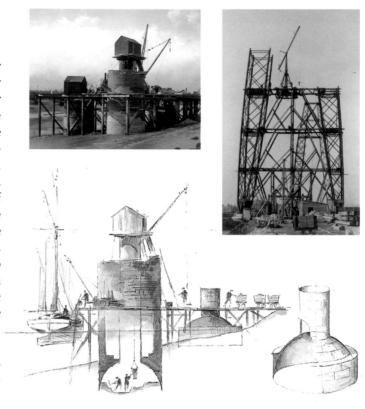

As each tower is in the form of a pair of legs set apart to allow the gondola to dock between, substantial temporary steel bracing was fixed to support them until they were jointed at the top.

Once the towers were complete and the suspension and anchor cables fixed, assembly of the boom was commenced, starting from the centre. First the main underframe forming the deep girders along which the traveller would run, was prefabricated on land, then raised in sections from barges moved into position as required. In this way, disruption of shipping was minimised. The sides and overhead stiffeners were then added, and all the cablework systematically tensioned to bring the boom to its correct alignment and firmness.

From this point of completion right back to the positioning of the first foundation caisson on the mud of the river, careful checking and measuring of each stage by engineers, had ensured that everything would come together correctly in the finished work. No life was lost in construction, which took four years.

Operation

In order to suit the times of shift-workers in nearby factories, the bridge operated daily from 5.45 am to 10.20 pm, making a crossing every 7½ minutes. It closed between 8 am and 1 pm on Sunday morning for maintenance. Warning that the bridge was closed was indicated by red flags flown from the motor-house and gondola, red lights on both sides of the motor-house, and a folding sign at the entrance to the eastern approach road. Originally, a very large red flag was flown from the centre of the boom, which, although much easier to see at a distance, proved inconvenient for the bridge crew. On royal birthdays and festive occasions the Union Jack was flown. During the wars the bridge worked throughout the night, except during air raids when sparks from the overhead trolleys would have served as a navigational aid to bomber crews. The carrying capacity is 6 cars and 120 people, or 13 tons. Only gale force winds cause it to close; neither ice nor fog being a problem. Very occasionally a delay may occur if one of the trolley-wheels comes off a power line. The maintenance man is then alerted by whistle from the gondola, and he goes to the motor-house where, by switching the power over to the controller there, he is able to drive the gondola to its destination. He then goes up and replaces the trolley-wheel while the gondola is docked. The bridge is also operated from the motor-house during maintenance, the men on the boom signalling required movements by whistle: two blasts for move eastwards, three for westwards, and one long blast for stop.

The bridge was manned on a shift system, each shift comprising of driver and conductor on the gondola, and a maintenance man usually in the workshop. The gondola crew wore uniforms supplied by the Borough Transport Department. The conductor was responsible for loading and unloading, operating the barriers, and issuing paper roll tickets. Although tolls were abolished in 1947, the charge of 'tops' money, for those wishing to cross via the boom, was retained. The driver was responsible for keeping to schedule, which he did by means of a clock in the pilot house. He may also originally have announced departures by ringing one of the bells. Apart from this gentle sound there is virtually no noise, vibration or unpleasant side-effect of any kind. Speed is about the same as a trotting horse, about 6½ mph (12 kph).

At the base of the western tower is a flat-roofed building (*left*). This is the Superintendent's Office, built in the 1950s to provide a base on the town side of the river, for crew and visiting officials. It is fitted with toilet and phone, and part of the ground floor is a waiting room for passengers. For passengers on the east bank, a wooden shed with bench seating and toilet was provided. This was located beside the motor-house, but was demolished around 1980.

Above: Typical industrial scene during the Bridge's heyday-Uskside Engineering & Rivet Works in 1912

Opposite top left and centre: Sinking the foundations
Opposite top right: Building the towers
Opposite below: Raising the boom

Waiting Room & Superintendents Office

Decline and Survival

So swift had been the growth of Newport, that even by the time the bridge was operational, developments were already taking place that were destined soon to undermine its viability. For whereas the first docks had been built upstream of the bridge as part of the old town with its established riverside wharves and canal, the later Alexandra Docks were progressively extended downstream. By 1914 they had direct access to the Bristol Channel by way of the South Lock - which, incidentally, was at that time the largest lock in the world. This was a great improvement as it reduced the amount of shipping needing to negotiate the tortuous Usk. As a result, the canal, riverside wharves and original Town Dock became obsolete. In 1930 this dock was filled in, followed by closure of other dock entrances onto the Usk, thus reducing river traffic still further.

In contrast to this progress on the west bank, developments on the east side lagged behind. For although much housing had been built on higher ground to the north, the anticipated expansion of industry, or development of any kind in the vicinity of the bridge, never fully took place, thus depriving the bridge of potential revenue.

Above: George Street Bridge

By far the greatest blow to the bridge was the dawning of the Motor Age. This grew relentlessly until, by 1960, a national network of motorways was beginning to take shape, and so, after all the port and railway improvements, it was the turn again of roads to be brought up to date. Clearly, a transporter bridge was not compatible with such a crowded and high speed system. This situation was remedied by the construction of George Street Bridge in 1964. By 1985, Newport Transporter Bridge lay idle. Closed for repairs, and overtaken by the swift tide of progress, it became a bridge on nobody's path; a bridge at a remote end of town, leading to a no-man's land. An austere grey structure straddling an austere grey river. One tower looming uncouthly over houses on the west bank, and the other, isolated on the vacant expanse of the east.

Left: View from George Street Bridge in 1988

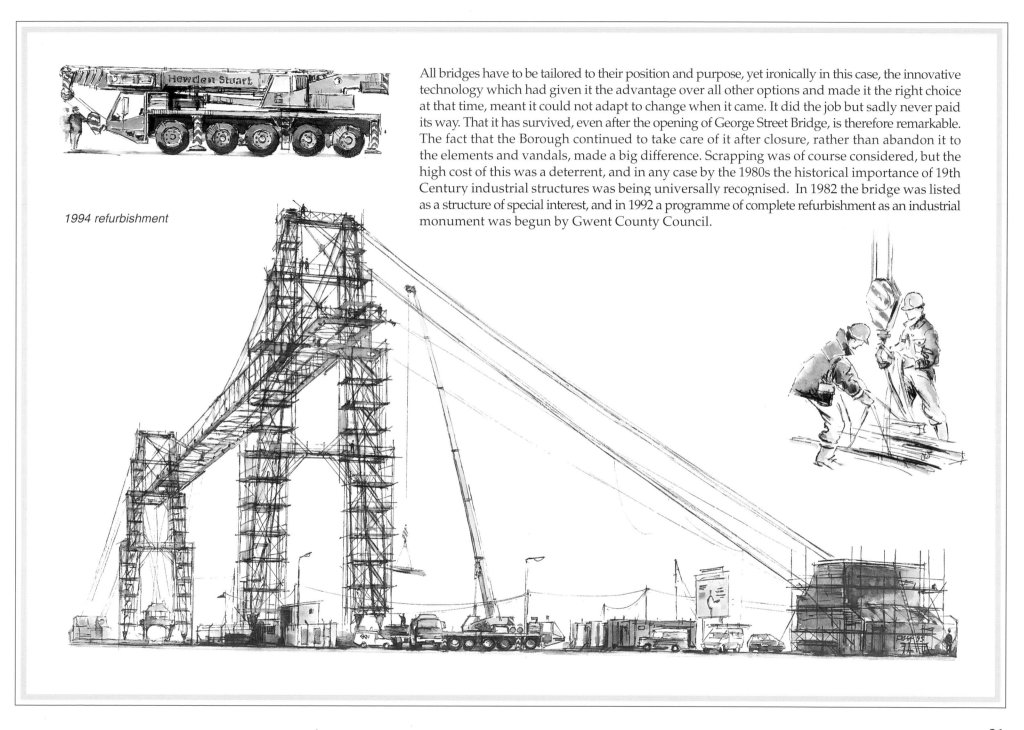

All bridges have to be tailored to their position and purpose, yet ironically in this case, the innovative technology which had given it the advantage over all other options and made it the right choice at that time, meant it could not adapt to change when it came. It did the job but sadly never paid its way. That it has survived, even after the opening of George Street Bridge, is therefore remarkable. The fact that the Borough continued to take care of it after closure, rather than abandon it to the elements and vandals, made a big difference. Scrapping was of course considered, but the high cost of this was a deterrent, and in any case by the 1980s the historical importance of 19th Century industrial structures was being universally recognised. In 1982 the bridge was listed as a structure of special interest, and in 1992 a programme of complete refurbishment as an industrial monument was begun by Gwent County Council.

1994 refurbishment

Transporter Bridges and Arnodin

Just as the castle, mentioned right at the beginning, is the last of a long line of fortresses which have occupied that site for over 2,000 years, so the Transporter Bridge is also one of the last of a line: a much shorter line though, of only 15 such bridges built worldwide, in the period of 23 years between 1893 and 1916. Of the six that are believed still to exist, three are in Britain, these being at Newport, Middlesborough, and a small privately owned one, now closed, at Warrington. The latter links two parts of the Crosfield Group Works over the Mersey and was the last transporter bridge to be built in the world. The longest was also across the Mersey, linking Runcorn to Widnes, having a span of 1,000 ft (305m). Neither were designed by Arnodin.

The principle of a transporter bridge had been known for some considerable time, and in the mid 1870s the British engineer, Charles Smith, had put forward a design for spanning the Tees at Hartlepool. However, it was Ferdinand Arnodin (1845-1924), a contemporary of Eiffel, who first put the idea into practice. This was in collaboration with Alberto del Palicio at Portugalete in Spain. Arnodin designed seven altogether of which Newport was his last and largest, and was opened when he was aged 60.

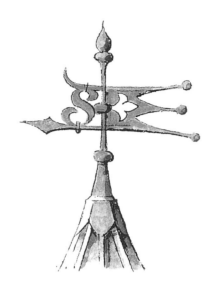

The Bridge Today

Ferdinand Arnodin

Newport Transporter Bridge is very much a product of its time; of the transitional period between horse-drawn vehicles and the pioneer motors, when handcarts for all types of business were common, and everyone either walked or cycled to work or went by tram. Built to permit the passage of the tallest fully-rigged ships, yet also to transport vehicles and passengers smoothly across mud and swirling waters at the mere turn of a small handle, it is one of the last structures of the old days of sail, and one of the first of the new age of mechanisation. All this is what gave it its unique form. Today it is seen as a milestone of transport technology at the turn of the century; a portal linking east and west, at the entrance to a once busy commercial highway - a symbol of the great days of sail and steam on the River Usk.

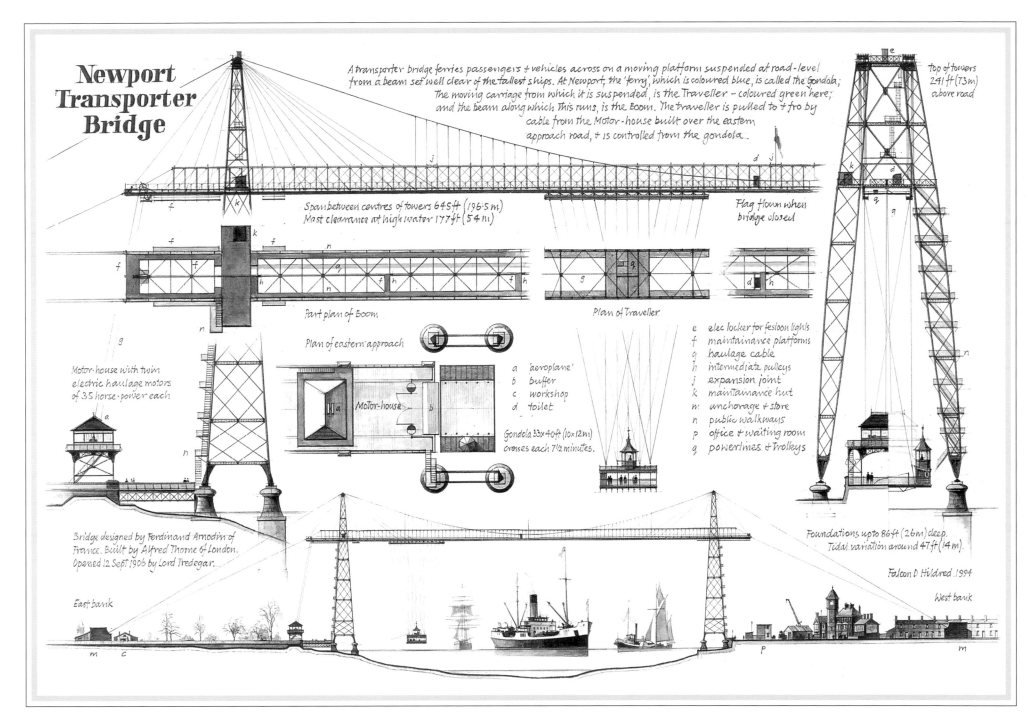

Newport Transporter Bridge

A transporter bridge ferries passengers & vehicles across on a moving platform suspended at road-level from a beam set well clear of the tallest ships. At Newport, the 'ferry', which is coloured blue, is called the Gondola; The moving carriage from which it is suspended, is the Traveller – coloured green here; and the beam along which this runs, is the Boom. The traveller is pulled to & fro by cable from the Motor-house built over the eastern approach road, & is controlled from the gondola.

top of towers 241 ft (73 m) above road

Span between centres of towers 645 ft (196·5 m)
Mast clearance at high water 177 ft (54 m)

Flag flown when bridge closed

Part plan of Boom

Plan of Traveller

Plan of eastern approach

Motor-house with twin electric haulage motors of 35 horse-power each

Motor-house

a 'aeroplane'
b buffer
c workshop
d toilet

Gondola 33 x 40 ft (10 x 12 m) crosses each 7½ minutes.

e elec locker for festoon lights
f maintainance platforms
g haulage cable
h intermediate pulleys
j expansion joint
k maintainance hut
m anchorage & store
n public walkways
p office & waiting room
q powerlines & trolleys

Bridge designed by Ferdinand Arnodin of France. Built by Alfred Thorne of London. Opened 12 Sept 1906 by Lord Tredegar.

East bank

Foundations up to 86 ft (26 m) deep.
Tidal variation around 47 ft (14 m).

Falcon D Hildred 1994

West bank

Sunset over the filled-in Town Dock, 1989

Author's Notes and Acknowledgements

In 1988 I was commissioned by Newport Museum and Art Gallery to make a pictorial study of Newport as part of the Museum's centenary celebrations. The project was jointly funded by Newport Borough Council and the Museums and Galleries Commission at the Victoria and Albert Museum, London. The resulting exhibition, called 'Newport Now', showed a typical 19th century industrial town adjusting to 20th century change. Among views of splendid town-centre buildings and a municipal park, which surely must be as fine as any in Britain, were drawings of steelworks, drydocks, scrapyards, and of course, the town's Transporter Bridge.

At that time, the bridge lay idle, with its future uncertain, and so it was in order to provide a record of this important but threatened structure that these drawings were made. Detailed though they were, many questions remained to be answered, and so it was that the work was extended, and eventually became this guidebook. In addition to the six main drawings shown in the original exhibition, and reproduced here on pages 5, 7, 9 etc, a number of site sketches and preliminaries have been included, together with a key plan and archive photographs so as to convey as full a picture as possible. Special care has been taken to present this information in a way which can be understood and enjoyed equally by the lay-person and expert.

To one whose work is all too often for the purpose of recording what is about to be destroyed, it is very rewarding on this occasion, to see these drawings being used in celebration of the bridge's refurbishment. The bridge was re-opened by Shadow Transport Secretary, Clare Short MP on 15 December 1995.

My thanks go to David Bassett and Maggie Urquhart, who, by their practical help and continued encouragement, enabled me to produce this book; Newport Borough Council, particularly Roger Cucksey for organising its publication, and the staff of Newport Reference Library; Gwent Record Office; and to Barry Mawson of Gwent Engineering Consultancy for helping me so generously. Finally, special thanks to John McDermott and Bill Collier for explaining the bridge to me, allowing full access, and sharing the welcome hospitality of their workshop.

Falcon D Hildred

Photo Rex Moreton

Falcon D Hildred was born in Grimsby in 1935 when it was the World's premier fishing town. From the very beginning he was fascinated by the sounds, shapes and smells of industry. He came to know other working towns - mill towns and mining towns - and he liked the way they were so open about what they did. The cranes and viaducts, terrace-houses and lines of washing, dialects and factory sirens, gave them integrity and identity, and a vitality which has now been lost. A wartime move to Coventry extended his interest, and it was here at the age of thirteen that he began his art training, which he completed at the Royal College of Art. Although an industrial designer by profession he now devotes much of his time to recording industrial archaeology, and has examples of his work in many national and local authority collections. In recognition of this work he was made an honorary member of the Royal Society of Architects in Wales. He now lives and works in a mill overlooking the slate-mining town of Blaenau Ffestiniog in North Wales, where he continues to add drawings to his Worktown exhibition.